Written by Andrew Brenner

Illustrations by Paul Gamble

Published by Pickwick Children's Entertainment, The Waterfront, Elstree, Hertfordshire, WD6 3BS.

# The Housekeeper

One day when I was clearing up
(It was a boring day)
I thought, "Why not build a robot
Which can put my toys away?"

So I took my father's tool kit
And I built this great machine
Which not only put my toys away
But also liked to clean

I programmed the whole house in
So it knew where things should be
But I forgot to programme in
A place for putting me!

Now my robot keeps things tidy
It would be my joy and pride
If it would open up the door
And let me back inside!

# The Pet-Walker

This is a robot for walking a dog
Which is also a robot for catching a frog
Inside of its belly is a tank for some fish
On top of its left foot is kitty's new dish

If you have a parrot there's a perch on its head
Open its mouth, that's a guinea pig's bed
There's a home for six mice inside each of its knees
But don't shake its hand, 'cause this robot has fleas

# The Sandwich-Maker

Hello … beep … please programme me
I'll make a sandwich for your tea
Push number 1 to choose your bread
Push 2 for toasted, 3 for spread

That's butter, mustard, margarine
Then … beep … choose what goes in between
If you want chicken please push 4
Or try my special: wild boar

Push number 5 if you like cheese
Do not push pepper or I sneeze
Push 6 for salad fresh and crunchy
Push 7 for my mystery munchy

Now use my letter keys to spell
Beep … other things you'd like as well
If … beep … your sandwich is too tall
Push 8 and I will squash it small

# The Quick-Shopper

I think this is terribly clever
Just watch when I pull this lever
That switches it on
See how quickly it's gone
Off to do all my shopping, wherever

This robot is enthusiastic
It's back now! Is that not fantastic?
But I don't believe this
It's forgotten my list
And instead bought some junk made of plastic!

# The Pizza-Deliverer

The pizza-robot's on the street
To bring the food you love to eat
He's faster than a motorbike
He knows which kind of sauce you like

He throws the dough as he zooms by
You'll see it spinning in the sky
Beneath the lamppost's golden light
There's pizza flying through the night

Then into his oven belly
Cheese, tomatoes, sausage smelly
When it's done in seconds flat
He throws it on your front door mat

And if you open up the door
The pizza skids across the floor
And if you stand in the wrong place
You catch the pizza in your face

Then as the robot speeds away
You put your pizza on a tray
There's no goodbyes, you have your plateful
Just eat your pizza and be grateful

# The Exam-Passer

I built a tiny robot
To take my test at school
I didn't want to study
I thought that I was cool

The teacher saw my robot
My test was incomplete
She said I was so clever
I didn't need to cheat

# The Chauffeur

Go robot go!
And don't go too slow
My uncle professor
Taught you all you know

Look out on the right!
Use your infra-red sight
You should slow down at least
When you reach a red light!

Stop robot stop!
That man is a cop
Don't go up the pavement
And look out for that shop!

Hello, officer, yes
I did make this mess
But it's my uncle's robot
So could he please confess?

# The Robot-Builder

This robot is wonderfully skilled
Because it is able to build
Another robot
Right here on the spot
Neatly welded and programmed and drilled

But if they carry on at that pace
We're soon going to run out of space
If they all make another
Mechanical brother
There'll be robots all over the place